TILLMAN'S

TREEHOUSE

Doc "O"

Glenhaven Publications: Seattle, Washington

Tillman's Treehouse

By Doc "O"

Published by:

Glenhaven Publications
P.O. Box 27841
Seattle Wa 98125-2841

Publisher's Cataloging-in-Publication
(Provided by Quality Books, Inc.)
Olson, Meredith Beach.
      Tillman's treehouse / Doc O.
      p. cm.
      SUMMARY: Tillman builds a treehouse where he can make
      interesting and useful contraptions.
      Preassigned LCCN: 97-93132
      ISBN 0-9657061-4-1 (softcover)
      ISBN 0-9657061-5-X (hardcover)

      1. Engineering--Juvenile fiction. 2. Creativity--Juvenile
      fiction. 3. Inventions--Juvenile fiction. I. Title

PZ7.05766Ti 1997   [Fic]
                       QBI97-40356

To almost everyone, Tillman's enthusiasm for building things was a nuisance. He was drawn instinctively to playing with water, air and materials. He loved things which moved. Most of his inventions were ingenious and quite buildable, though he often had to overcome technical difficulties. Discussing his mechanical dilemmas drew his mother, father, and friends into the design of clever contraptions.

dedicated
to
Jim Tillman
who has spent the last twenty years
trying to understand
dust storms on Mars

Visit the Web

See Tillman's Treehouse
on the
University of Washington Atmospheric Sciences home page
http://www-k12.atmos.washington.edu/k12/

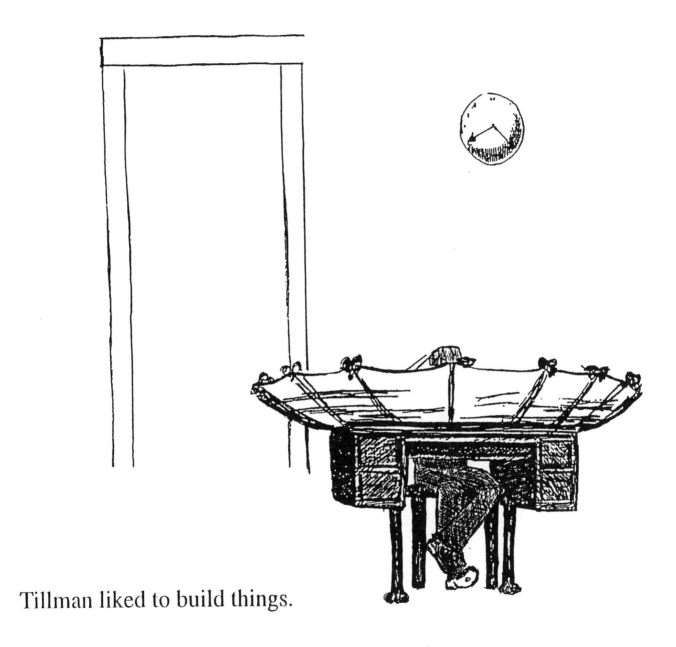

Tillman liked to build things.

Sometimes he built helpful things at school.

Although the merry-go-round Tillman built on his school desk allowed him to have the proper textbook in front of him at all times, his teacher found it a nuisance.

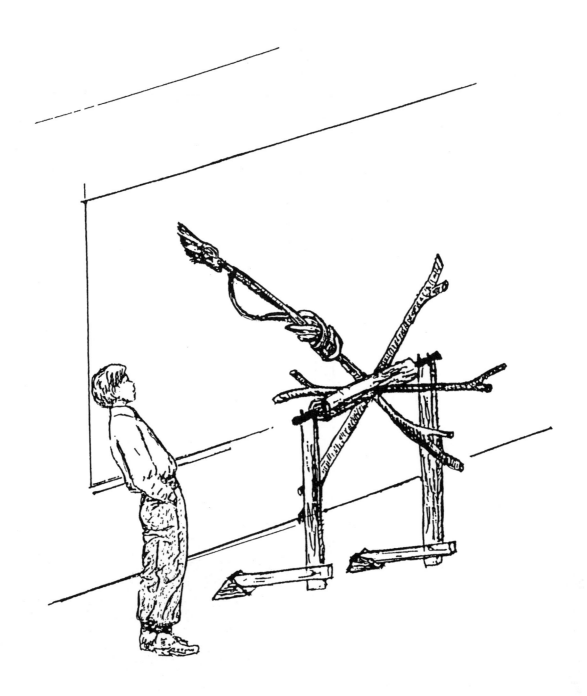

The custodian was not pleased with Tillman's automatic blackboard washer.

The automatic bell ringer Tillman made for the Principal had many fine features, but the Principal was annoyed with it. She told Tillman to go outside and play the way other students did.

The bus driver said that Tillman simply had to leave his tools and equipment at home so there would be enough room for other students on the bus.

Tillman didn't watch
television.

He always had plenty of things
he wanted to do. He decided that
he needed his own corner of the yard
in which to do them.

He chose a far corner, away from the stop signs and the traffic. His
corner had three trees and a fine fence on two sides. It had a brook
running kitty-corner through a little meadow. The sun warmed
the grass and made it a nice place to be.

One of his trees was quite tall with a trunk which went straight up.
It was very strong. Tillman walked right over to the thick
tree trunk and put down his tools.

He began to plan a very high treehouse where he could stay out of
other people's way.

He set to work. Before long he had made a fine floor with triangular braces so it would not sway in the wind. He made a sloped roof to keep the rain out.

His high treehouse allowed him to look down on the rooftops of the neighborhood. He looked for materials to use in the contraptions he wanted to build.

His special corner of the yard had a little region of sand
which gathered into tiny dunes when the wind blew.
On hot days Tillman liked to stand on the burning sand
 with his knees cooled by the breeze.

He often thought about dust storms on Mars.
He wondered what it would be like to stand on soil
which had a millimeter thick layer of 60 degree soil
with freezing temperatures at his knees.

Tillman liked to read about Mars.
He knew dust storms sometimes covered
the entire planet up to the very tops of the
huge mountains.   Dust is tiny and can
be whipped up by the thin atmosphere.

Sand is another matter. It is heavy.
Sand can't be lifted by the thin Martian atmosphere.

He wondered what it would be like to stand on Mars
with raging sand storms up to his ankles.

Tillman often came out to his treehouse at night
to look at Mars
and think about what it was like there.

The running brook gurgled invitingly so Tillman's
first project was to find a way to make the brook flow
into pieces of gutters left over from the
neighbor's roof repair project.

He propped the ends of gutter pieces with forked sticks.
Little waterfalls fell from one gutter to the next.
He controlled the flow by raising and lowering the ends.

He wanted water to flow fast. He wanted it to flow slowly.
He made several different arrangements
trying to make the water flow change.

Although he couldn't bring his gutters and pipes to school, Tillman had his brain with him and could think about his design. He found the speed of flow of several large rivers of the world on the computer. He wondered how he could design channels to move faster (or slower) than these rivers.

Tillman found these web sites gave him some interesting information:

http://h2o.usgs.gov/public/realtime.html
http://txwww.cr.usgs.gov/pubs/circular/1123/abstract.html
http://wwwdwatcm.wr.usgs.gov

All that work with running water and falling water gave
Tillman some ideas.   He decided to make a water wheel.

Tillman decided that he
needed large paddles for steady currents.
Using the wheels from a broken bicycle, he
made an "undershot" wheel where the water flowed under
the wheel.   The wheel turned slowly but powerfully. He could
lift water way up high to use for his projects.

Water left over from his projects could fall a long way. He made an "overshot" wheel which let the water fall on it from above. The wheel turned very fast.

Tillman liked kites. Could water
wheels make kites fly?
Maybe the wheel should
turn sideways instead of
up and down.

With more effort and cleverness,
he managed to build a vertical axle
water wheel.

He discovered it is important for the wheel
to have good bearnings. Even with wood attached,
his old bike wheels turned smoothly.

"It's the bearings, Silly"

Tillman liked to look inside rocks and nuts.

He made a water wheel out of huge spoons.
It turned a big wheel with a heavy collar
on the center post.

He found
he could
grind nuts
by pouring
them
in the
center

Tillman didn't always have wood to work with.
He asked his neighbors to save plastic bottles for him.
He needed the caps too.

Tillman carefully cut off the bottom of each bottle.
When he screwed on the cap he had an upside-down
water container. It also made a fine funnel.

He made a wheel with plastic bottles.

Sometimes he found piles of left over boxes.
His long, skinny plastic boxes
were sturdy and waterproof.

He made a wheel with compartments

Tillman found his water wheel could make things work.

He could make hammers pound clay into nice shapes.

His water wheel could take him to distant places.

Tillman loved flowing water. He wondered how fast it went.
He liked to toss leaves in the river and watch them speed away.
Tillman thought about that. How could he build a speedometer
to tell him how fast the river flowed?

Tillman decided to try to build an underwater wheel.

He shaped it like an airplane propeller and attached it to a heavy pipe on the stream bottom.

He found he could measure the speed of water current with this contraption

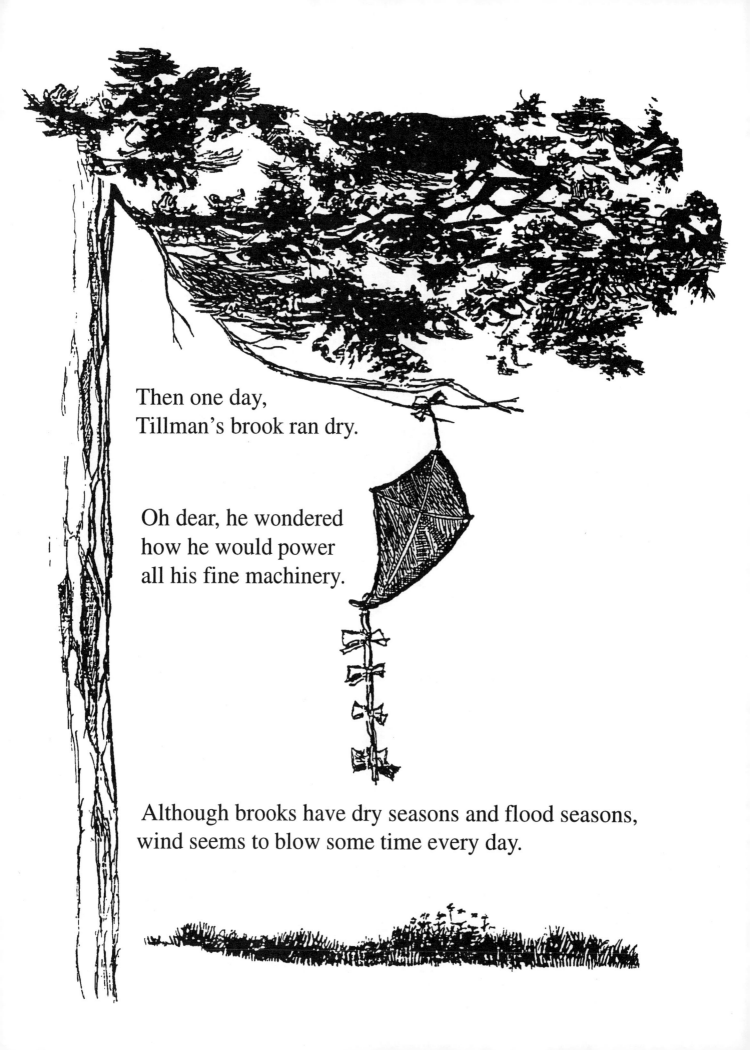

Then one day,
Tillman's brook ran dry.

Oh dear, he wondered
how he would power
all his fine machinery.

Although brooks have dry seasons and flood seasons,
wind seems to blow some time every day.

Tillman began to consider how to use his wheels
to capture the power of the wind. His treehouse
was up very high and was far away from buildings
which might block the wind. First he made a wind-ball
to see if he could detect breezes.

Then he made parachutes
to see if wind or air could change the way things fall.

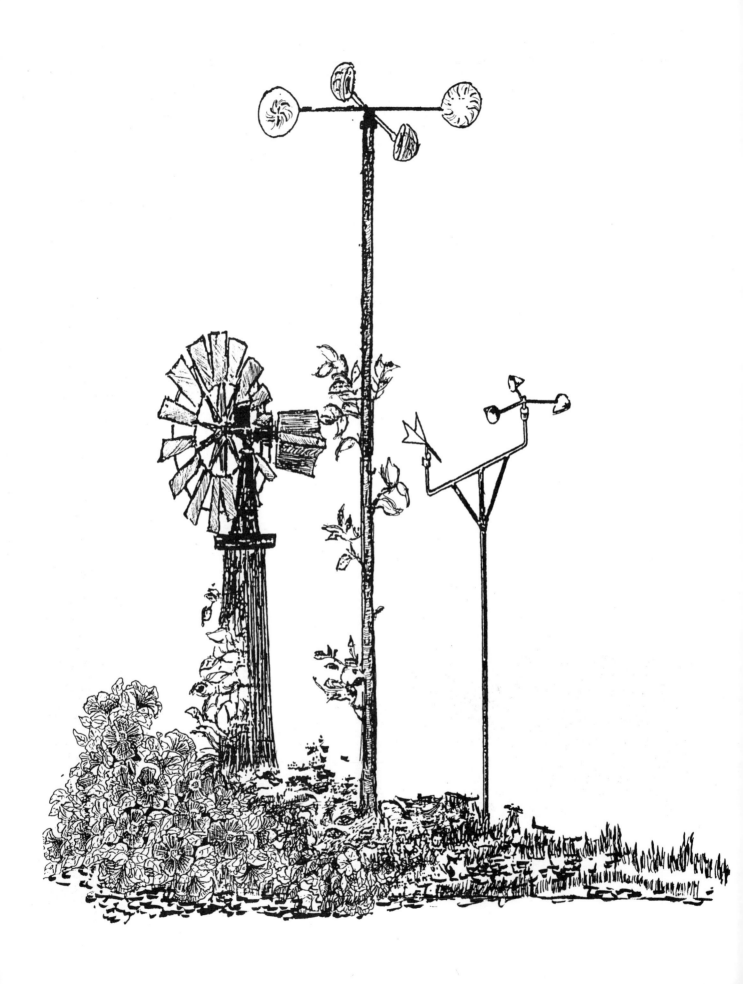

His wind wheels and propellers
used the clever ideas
he had developed for water power.

His Dutch windmill needed sails
to make it work in light breezes.

Tillman had trouble with wind direction.
He found that wind does not always
come from the same direction the way water does.
He had to make a propeller wind-vane
so his rig would turn to face the wind.

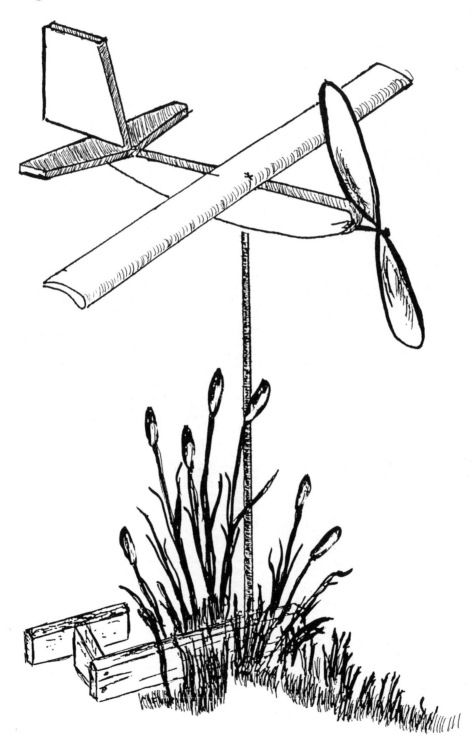

Tillman wanted to scare away the birds who scattered
his screws and nails. He combined ideas from his
wind-vanes and wind wheels. He made a noisy
KALPOTEZ just like those used in Austria.

http://bau2.uibk.ac.at/guerti.oesterreich/austria.html

Tillman decided he would have his own contest. He wanted to know whether his fine wind-vane would agree with the wind-vane atop the university building. Tillman put a large foil pizza pan on the ground around the base of his wind-vane. He used his orienteering compass to locate directions north, south, east and west.   Each day Tillman recorded where the wind was coming from.

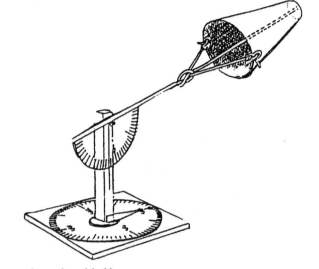

On a computer he found
this web site gave him
wind direction on top of the university building.

http://www.atmos.washington.edu/

He made a data table to compare the wind directions at his treehouse and at the university. He was pleased that his wind-vane agreed so well with the fancy university equipment.

Tillman liked to look at clouds. He checked cloud patterns every morning from his treehouse. When he got to school he looked at the University of Washington Red Square camera monitor so see if the clouds were the same across town.

http://www.washington.edu/

He remembered his trip to Hawaii and liked to see the current weather conditions in his favorite places. He typed the web site:

http://weather.satlab.hawaii.edu

He loved to see the rainfall maps of various western states. He typed:

http://www.ocs.arst.edu/prism/mt_precip.gif

Three other www locations had great pictures if you clicked on enough words.

http://www.weather.com/weather/

http://www.wsdot.wa.gov/regions/northwest/nwflow/

http://www.wadot.wa.gov/regions/northwest/NWFLOW/camera/
vidframe.html

When he was in a building mood, Tillman often examined the way NOAA launched drifting buoys just before a Hurricane so it could make barometer readings, wind measurements and wave measure-ments. He typed:

http://seaboard.ndba.noaa.gov/drift.html
or
http://seaboard.ndbc.noaa.gov

Now he had all the power he needed and he had peace and quiet to set out his supplies and work on his projects. Tillman was pleased to have such a fine treehouse where he could build his things.

And his classmates and even his teacher dropped by frequently to see what he was building next.

About the Author

Doctor Meredith Olson, known affectionately as Doc "O" to her students, has taught middle school and high school math and science in Seattle, Washington for 40 years. Her primary goal is the improvement of pre-college Engineering education. By going to lab to work on contraptions every day, her students come to understand properties of the mechanical world. In addition to classroom teaching, Doc "O" is currently the Project Educator for the Mars Exploration Program of Jet Propulsion Laboratory and a curriculum developer for national public television. She works with universities, museums, and school districts throughout the country to promote improvement in science instruction. She believes that children must construct their own understanding from active design and assemblage of contraptions. By testing, failing, remodeling, and trying again, we come to **see** the structures we are looking at. Children begin to understand the engineering process. Besides, it's fun.

While expressing an appreciation of the beautiful world around us, this book explores engineering fantasies of children.

Order Form

Fax orders: (206) 362-2265

Postal orders: Glenhaven Publications
                       P.O. Box 27841-110
                       Seattle WA, 98125-2841

Name:_____

Address:_____

City:_____   State:_____   Zip:_____

Phone: (_____) _____

Please send the following books:

Titles	Qty
Tillman's Treehouse	____
Page's Pencilsharpener	____
_____	____
_____	____

Tax: Add 8.20% to books shipped to Washington State addresses.

Shipping:
    Book Rate: $2.00 first book, $0.75 each additional (allow 3-4 wks).
    Air mail: $3.50 per book.

Payment:
    Check__   (pay to: Glenhaven Publications)
    VISA__   Mastercard__

    Card number: _____

    Name on card: _____   Exp. date: ____/____

Available Summer 1997

Introducing

Page's Pencilsharpener

the next book in the Doc "O" series

This book is about pencil sharpeners. They seem so simple. We know that pencils are the most widely used tool for writing and drawing in the world today. More than two billion pencils are sold in the United States each year. They have to be sharpened. We find sharpeners everywhere - but have we looked at them? How much do we comprehend of what a pencil sharpener does? What do children notice? What do they understand?

This is not a book full of experiments. This is sort of a story book; a kind of a guided observation book which allows us to see when we look. Parents don't have to feel the obligation to set up equipment and clean up messes. That is not the point. The point is to observe. A sharpener seems so simple. There are only about a dozen parts but how do we learn to see them?

The intention of this book is not to read it from cover to cover but for the adult to read with the child - to help the child become more observant of the world around. When reading with children, give them what they want. What do they choose to look at? Do they ask you to read the printed words or just talk about the ideas? Do they want to read to the end of the book? Do they show interest in just half the book? Maybe just one page?

By asking questions you might inspire the child to observe a pencil sharpener & come back & observe & come back. What is the angle of a gear? Are they both set the same? Do they taper? Which direction is the taper of the hole? Why does pencil stop when it is sharp? Are the gear threads equally sharp in both directions? Do pencils sharpen equally well when the handle is turned clockwise or counter-clockwise? How many ways are pencils sharpener fixed to the wall? Our discussions might include observing together and reflecting on how they cleverly solved each problem. After reflecting on an idea, the child may try making a contraption similar to that depicted, but most children do not. More often we find children developing their imaginations and their creative dreams of future projects. They dream of wonderful contraptions in a world of natural beauty. By counterposing the natural world and the designed world in these sketches, we help children see the beauty in each.

Order Form

Fax orders: (206) 362-2265

Postal orders: Glenhaven Publications
P.O. Box 27841-110
Seattle WA, 98125-2841

Name:_____

Address:_____

City:_____ State:_____ Zip:_____

Phone: (_____) _____

Please send the following books:

Titles	Qty
Tillman's Treehouse	____
Page's Pencilsharpener	____
_____	____
_____	____

Tax: Add 8.20% to books shipped to Washington State addresses.

Shipping:

Book Rate: $2.00 first book, $0.75 each additional (allow 3-4 wks).
Air mail: $3.50 per book.

Payment:

Check__   (pay to: Glenhaven Publications)

VISA__   Mastercard__

Card number: _____

Name on card: _____ Exp. date: ____/____

The Philosophy Behind The Doc "O" Series

These books are intended to be more than children's story books. They are more than picture books. They are crafted to draw a child's attention to what is subtle and significant in the designed world, and to use that awareness to imagine ingenious adaptations. The refinement of perception is fundamental to the development of human intelligence.

Each book is designed to promote engagement and discussion. Children need opportunities to develop the habit of attention, observe minute points of accuracy, and develop the art of expression as they discuss these ideas with adults. When, by repeated little observations, we train the eye to notice subtle attributes, we develop the child's ability to devise new ways of using familiar objects.

How long does it take to train the eye? Throughout forty years of science teaching, I have noticed that it takes students about three days of class activity (and evening incubation time) to begin to comprehend what should be noticed. Three 10 minute sessions are more powerful than a 30 minute session. Understanding seems to come in three waves. We need to know where to look. We need to know how to look. We need to imagine possibilities beyond what is currently observable.

When we make decisions about what we will read with the child, we make decisions about their future interests and success in life. The pictures presented here are composed to help the child to see both nature and the designed world as objects of beauty. We want the child to see human ingenuity as a work of art.

Why Read Doc "O" Books With Your Child?

The absence of an opportunity for your child to think about the designed world can have profound consequences. By reading and discussing the ideas included in the Doc "O" books, you will enhance your children's confidence and joy in their own reasoning abilities.